First Steps to
CHI KUNG

Master K. Y. Wong

AXIOM

ISBN: 1 86476 034 6

Axiom
Australia

Chi in
Chinese
means Air,
but the meaning is more in
Chi Kung

Contents page

Chi Kung

was created through the composite experience of a long-term struggle by the Chinese people to work in harmony with nature. It not only plays an important role in strengthening the health of the individual and thus preventing many diseases, but also helps in treating many illnesses and prolonging life.

Master Wong Kuan-Yew - Brief Biography

In 1970, while playing basketball for the University of Malaya, Wong Kuan-Yew injured his knee and for years after was barely able to walk without intense pain. In 1975 a friend told him of an exceptional tai chi master who was also a practitioner of Chinese medicine. The problem was Master Huang Shing-Seang would only treat his students and not outsiders. Wong Kuan-Yew enrolled in classes in order to get the medical treatment, not out of any special interest in tai chi. However Master Huang was a wise man and informed his impatient new pupil that six months' practice of tai chi would be needed to effect a cure for the knee. He did not offer any Chinese medical treatment. Wong Kaun-Yew, having no other choice, buckled down to the regular practice and found his knee problem cured in less than six months. In his own words: "I trusted the 'miracle' power of tai chi from that day onwards."

It was the beginning of a lifelong journey, in which his deep command of classical Chinese language helped him gain a profound understanding of tai chi and chi kung principles and philosophy. His cultural background and education had made him deeply respectful towards all his instructors, resulting in relationships which have gone far beyond the normal master/student association.

Since 1975, Master Wong has had the privilege, granted only to a very few, of having the opportunity to learn from several world top grandmasters. Grandmaster Huang Shing-Seang, as previously mentioned, was his first master, teaching Yang style tai chi and philosophy. It was with Grandmaster Huang that Master Wong's skill received its foundation, in particular his understanding of the concept of 'sung' (relaxation and looseness).

The greatest influence on Master Wong has been his current master, the present world premier and keeper of Chen style tai chi, Grandmaster Chen Xiao-Wang, who is the 19th generation direct descendent of the family which created tai chi. From him, Master Wong has learned the origin of all aspects of tai chi - the Chen style itself, chi kung, push hands, tai chi chin-na (grappling), fajing (explosive tai chi power), philosophy and all essences of the art.

His other masters include Grandmaster Fong Lam, from whom he deepened his knowledge of chi kung; Grandmaster Chok Seng-Kam (Yang style tai chi), and senior coach of China, Grandmaster Bai Wei-Xiang, who taught him Soon style tai chi.

Although he adheres strictly to chi kung and tai chi principles, both mentally and spiritually, Master Wong has evolved a unique teaching style. Many of his students claim to have recovered from chronic ailments after learning chi kung and tai chi from him. Some who were weak initially have gained in strength and general health, while sports persons and martial artists of different disciplines have improved their stability, flexibility and strength after studying with Master Wong for only a short period. His teaching encompasses the complete tai chi/chi kung system, including health, martial art and philosophical aspects.

Master Wong is married with four children. The entire family is involved in tai chi and chi kung, living according to the principles and reaping the benefits. They moved to Australia in 1988 in order to enhance the children's education and career prospects. At the time Master Wong was a businessman and had been teaching tai chi and chi kung in Malaysia after business hours. Once established in Australia, Grandmaster Chen Xiao-Wang encouraged him to commence teaching again. As class numbers grew it became obvious to Master Wong he could not carry out his business duties as well as put in the enormous amount of practice required to keep up standards he regards as necessary to be an effective teacher. In 1992 he gave up his business interests and dedicated his life to teaching tai chi and chi kung. In this way, he is carrying on the tradition of his father, and at the same time making a significant contribution to the community in which he has chosen to live.

Forward

Qigong, also written as Chi Kung, has been practiced by Chinese for more than 3000 years. There are many types of Chi Kung, with more than 2000 already documented.

Tai Chi Chi Kung 18 Movements, or 'Shibashi' for short, was founded by Dr Lim Hou Shen of China. "My master, Fong Lam, learnt privately from Dr Lim and together with him, spread this style of Chi Kung exercise to Japan".

Tai Chi Chi Kung 18 Movements is easy to learn. It helps improve health and prevent illness if practiced correctly and diligently.

Tai Chi Chi Kung 18 Movements is the most popular Chi Kung in many Asian countries including Japan, Malaysia, Indonesia, Singapore and Thailand. It is the most popular Chi Kung in Australia.

Australian Ying Yang Tai Chi Academy in which Master Wong is the founder and chief instructor was the first in Australia to stress that students learn the Tai Chi Chi Kung 18 Movements before studying Tai Chi. Many students have claimed recovery from various illnesses after practicing this style of Chi Kung for only a few weeks .

Although many are teaching Tai Chi Chi Kung, most do not fully understand the philosophy of this style of Chi Kung. Although teaching arm movements, they do not understand the actual Tai Chi principles within Chi Kung, consequently the full benefits are not realised.

Master Wong was prompted to write this book by his desire to have as many people as possible benefit from this easy to learn form of Chi Kung. It is also a direct way to express his thanks to Chi Kung master and the Founder, Dr Lim. At the same time, he would like those instructors who are already teaching this Chi Kung to understand the Tai Chi principles involved, enabling them to instruct their own students correctly. It is therefore hoped that the good name of this rich cultural Chinese heritage will not be tarnished .

Relaxation
is the route to longevity.
Stress is the root of all illness.
-Chinese saying

Chi Kung is one of five disciplines of Chinese cultural heritage. The others being Chinese Medicine, I-Ching, Tao-Te Ching and Tai Chi.

Chi Kung was created through the composite experience of a long struggle by the Chinese people to work in harmony with nature. It not only plays an important role in strengthening the health of the individual and thus preventing many diseases, but also helps in treating many illnesses and prolonging life.

Chi in Chinese means Air, but the meaning is more than simply Air in Chi Kung.

Chi Kung, in Chinese means Breathing Work or Breathing Exercise. But, in fact, it is much more than just a breathing exercise.

Chi is material based. The Chi of a Chi Kung practitioner contains static electricity, infra-red, magnetism, etc. It is an energy, the biological or vital energy of the human body. Chi in Chi Kung is not limited to just the inhaling or exhaling of air.

Chi Kung

In Chinese medical theories, Chi is more important than blood. Chi leads the blood to flow. If one is lacking in blood; by an infusion, one can regain normal levels. If one is lacking in Chi, ie no biological energy in the heart cells, the heart will not pump and the blood not flow. Therefore, without Chi, there will be death. If Chi is weak, the body will be weak.

There are twelve main meridians and eight secondary meridians through which Chi flows. If Chi flows through the meridians smoothly, the body will be healthy. If Chi does not flow smoothly in the meridians, being restricted or blocked, the body will be sick.

In Chinese medical theories, causes of diseases are internal and external.

Internal refers to the seven emotions, they are: joy; anger; grief; excess thinking; sadness; fear and terror. The emotion causes Chi changes, thus affecting the functions of various organs. Research in modern medicine found that 50% - 80% of disorders such as kidney diseases, hypertension, heart diseases, ulcers and cancer, etc are all commonly caused by stress.

External causes of diseases are the four seasons, and six kinds of weather changes:- wind; cold; heat; wetness; dryness and fire. These affect the body's adaptability and resistance. Pathogenic diseases are related to the extreme weather changes which help to promote, multiply and spread disease.

Chi Kung exercise is different from other medical treatment, either eastern or western. It does not depend on anything or anyone else. It is 'self help' therapy. It has no side-effects and as long as the practitioner is correctly taught, then practices with patience and perseverance, Chi Kung exercise will help strengthen the body and in some cases prevent and even cure disease.

There are three important aspects to Chi Kung practice.
1. Regulating of the mind - It is important to have a 'relaxed' mind and 'relaxed' physical body before starting the Chi Kung exercises.

When the mind is tranquil, the cerebral cortex is in a 'rested' state and can regulate the central nervous system and thus promote proper function of the organs.

The 'relaxed' body will promote the Chi flow in the meridians.

There are many methods to achieve the above and in this book, the Physical Portion Relaxation Technique is introduced.

2. Regulating of the body - Different Chi Kung exercises have different demands in the movement or positioning of the body. It is important for Chi Kung practitioners to know and understand the philosophy and the requirement of the type of Chi Kung, because correct postures and body movement relates to proper Chi flow.

3. Regulating of the breath - Since Chi Kung means 'breathing exercise', regulating of the breath is, as one would expect, of utmost importance.

Generally, there are two types of breathing.
(a) Normal rib cage breathing
When breathing in, the rib cage expands and diaphragm pulls down 1 or 2 cm. When breathing out, the rib cage and diaphragm go back to the normal position. This type of breathing is shallow. Under normal conditions, the rate of breathing in, and breathing out, is 16-18 times/minute. During resting or sleeping, the rate is slightly lower. During exercise, the rate will increase.

(b) Diaphragm breathing
In Chi Kung or Tai Chi practice, deep diaphragm breathing is encouraged.

During the intake with diaphragm breathing the diaphragm is pulled down much more, 4 to 6, or 8 to 10 cm. The rib cage expands very little, if at all. The stomach expands when breathing in.

During breathing out with diaphragm breathing, the diaphragm and rib cage return to normal and the stomach relaxes. Therefore, diaphragm breathing is also referred to as 'stomach breathing'.

The advantage of diaphragm breathing are as follows:

(a) For every centimetre of diaphragm pulled down during the breathing in, the volume of air in the lungs increases by about 300 c.c., on average. If the diaphragm is constantly pulled down by 6-10 cm, the amount of air in the lung increases many fold. When there is more air in the lung, the blood will become more oxygenated. There will be more oxygen to be carried to the brain cells and all parts of the body. This helps to enhance memory, increase alertness and create more energy. Therefore, Chi Kung practitioners are energetic, alert, and more active.

(b) It helps increase the immune system of the body. Many forms of bacteria and germs do not multiply under aerobic conditions. It is proven even cancer cells do not multiply when there is increased oxygen. In China, for cancer patients, chemotherapy and Chi Kung exercise are used for treatment.

(c) The rise and fall of the diaphragm serves to massage all the internal organs such as stomach, spleen, pancreas, large and small intestines. The functions of the internal organs are normal if they are in a healthy condition. This reduces the chances of physiological disorders such as gastric, diabetes, constipation, etc.

(d) Diaphragm breathing serves to cool down the central nervous system and can bring 'calmness' and 'tranquillity' to the mind.

With all of these advantages and knowing our air is free, everyone should practice Chi Kung exercises with full diaphragm breathing and enjoy the benefits of greater health.

Physical Portion Relaxation Technique

Relaxation is very important for good Chi Kung practice. In fact, it is the prerequisite of Chi Kung exercise. There are many relaxation techniques. Below is one of the simplest and yet most effective - Physical Portion Relaxation Technique.

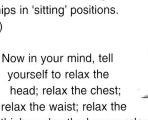

- Stand with feet apart, approximately at shoulder width.
- Maintain a straight posture, knees naturally bent, head upright, hands besides the thighs and with hips in 'sitting' positions. (Fig 1 & 2)

Fig 1

Now in your mind, tell yourself to relax the head; relax the chest; relax the waist; relax the thighs; relax the knees; relax the lower legs and relax the feet. Your mind moves down from head to feet to completely relax the entire body as you command yourself.

After that, tell yourself to relax the shoulders; relax the upper arms; relax the lower arms; relax the fingers. As before, your mind keeps moving down from the shoulders to the fingers as you command it.

Now your whole body is relaxed (you can repeat the commands two or three times) with your entire body weight at the bottom of your feet.

Fig 2

Diaphragm Breathing Technique

Diaphragm Breathing Technique

As already mentioned diaphragm breathing is one of the important processes in Chi Kung practice. Below is one of the diaphragm breathing training exercises which may further assist you.

After the Portion Physical Relaxation Techniques, continue with the diaphragm breathing training.

Place the palms 2 to 3 inches below the navel (fig 3).

The mind is in the area where the palms touch.

Fig 3

Concentrate on diaphragm breathing, ie when breathing in, the stomach expands, when breathing out, the stomach contracts. The palms will feel the 'up' and 'down' of the stomach when breathing. The breathing must be slow, even, fine and deep.

- Do not force the breathing.
- Do not use the chest to breathe (ie chest expands when you breathe in and contracts when you breathe out). The diaphragm breathing must be in a relaxed manner.

Do not allow the mind to wander. Always bring it back to the area where your palms touch.

Stay calm, relax and practice the diaphragm breathing everyday for 10 to 15 minutes before starting your Tai Chi Chi Kung 18 Movements.

Tai Chi Chi Kung 18 Movements (Shibashi)

Tai Chi Chi Kung 18 Movements is a Chi Kung exercise but **not** Tai Chi. It is a type of Chi Kung based on Tai Chi principles. Its most basic principles are:

- Body straight, but relaxed
- All movements initiate from the feet, waist or body (not hands)
- All movements with controlled breathing in and out
- All breathing from the diaphragm

Tai Chi Chi Kung 18 Movements (Shibashi) if practiced correctly and diligently can have the following benefits:

- All the benefits of diaphragm breathing as discussed
- Good posture and improvement of back problems
- Regulated blood pressure and heart rate
- Increased 'Chi' (vital energy or bio electric energy) flow
- Assistance with certain arthritis and shoulder problems
- Strengthen the legs and waist
- Improved blood circulation
- Improved digestion and regular bowel habit
- Strengthen the kidney functions
- Reduced tiredness and revitalised muscle function
- Increased mental tranquillity
- Improved balance and flexibility

The number of repetitions in each movement is not important as long as there is continuity in the form and the correct breathing in and out during the movements.

1. To Begin and Regulate Breathing

(a) Feet apart shoulder width with hands besides the thighs (fig 4). Relax all the portions of the body with knees naturally bent.

Fig 4

Fig 5

(b) Raise the body slowly and very slowly raise the arms until shoulder height and width (fig 5 & 6), breathing in at the same time.

Fig 6

Important:- arms should not be straightened, the elbows are slightly bent and the wrists relaxed with fingers facing downwards.

1. To Begin and Regulate Breathing

Fig 7

(c) Sink the body down slightly with knees bent, followed by shoulders, elbows and wrists. Fingers should be pointing upwards and forwards (fig 7), breathing out once you start to sink the body.

Fig 8

(d) Continue sinking the body moving both arms down to the thighs, still breathing out until the arms touch the thighs (fig 8)

> **Important:-** the lowest the body should sink is to the point where the knees and toes are in one line. If bent until the knees are in front of the toes additional and undesirable pressure is placed on the knees.

2.To Expand the Chest

Fig 9

Fig 10

(a) Start as in Fig 9

(b) Raise the body slowly and very slowly raise the arms until shoulder height and width (fig 10). Breathing in at the same time.

Fig 11

Fig 12

(c) Turn the palms with fingers facing each other (fig 11), still breathing in.

(d) Stretch out the arms, as you continue breathing in, until the arms extend each side of the body (fig 12).

Important:- shoulders, elbows and chest should be relaxed, and arms slightly bent.

2.To Expand the Chest

(e) Both palms swing forward at the wrist like door hinges, (fig 13) and you start breathing out.

(f) Both arms are brought forward with palms facing each other, shoulder height and width (fig 14), continue breathing out.

(g) Turn both palms with fingers facing forward and upward (fig 15), still breathing out.

(h) Sink the body down slightly to bring the arms down to the sides of the thighs (fig 16), gradually breathing out all the time.

3. To Wave The Rainbow

Fig 17

(a) To continue the movement shown at Fig 16.

(b) Very slowly raise the arms upwards from the front of the body to above the head (fig 17), breathing in as the arms are raised.

(c) Shift the weight to the right leg as the body turns slightly to the left. At the same time, drop the left arm downward to the left of the body with palm facing upwards (palm and left shoulder are at the same level with left elbow slightly bent) and the right arm moves to the top of the head with the palm facing downward (fig 18), still breathing in.

Fig 18

20

3. To Wave The Rainbow

(d) Shift the body weight to the centre and return the arms to the top (fig 19). Breathing out when starting to shift the weight.

(e) Shift the weight to the left leg and the body turns slightly to the right. At the

Fig 19

Fig 20

same time, drop the right arm downward to the right of the body with palm facing upwards (palm and shoulder at same level with elbow slightly bent) and the left arm moves to the top of the head with palm facing downward (fig 20), still breathing out.

Important:- When moving the arms to the right and left, the eyes must look at the extended palms and make sure the knees are slightly bent and the waist is curved slightly.

4. To Circulate The Arms For Separating The Cloud

(a) Continue from the previous posture

(b) Shift the weight to the centre (equal weight on each leg) and bring the arms to the top (fig 21). Breathe in when starting to shift weight.

Fig 21

Fig 22

(c) Turn the palms facing outward and slightly forwards (Fig 22), still breathing in.

(d) Body starts to sink down (bend knees) and bring the arms downwards (fig 23). Breathing out once you start to sink the body.

Fig 23

4. To Circulate The Arms For Separating The Cloud

(e) Move the arms to cross in front of the body with the right palm below the left (both facing upwards) (fig 24). Still breathing out.

(f) Move the body upwards (standing up slightly) so as

Fig 24

Fig 25

to push the arms upward (still with palms facing upwards) (Fig 25), breathe in once you start to move the body upwards.

(g) Once the palms rise to chest level, turn them upwards while the arms continue to move up (fig 26) still breathing in.

Fig 26

5. Fixed Stance With Back Rolling Of Upper Arms

Fig 27

(a) Continue from the previous posture.

(b) Body sinks down slightly with the palms facing outward and slightly forwards, and the arms stretching outwards (Fig 27), breathing out once the body starts to sink down.

Fig 28

Fig 29

(c) Both arms are brought to shoulder height and width with palms facing each other (fig 28), still breathing out.

(d) Shift weight to the left and waist turns right, bring the right arm down to the side (fig 29), still breathing out.

24

5. Fixed Stance With Back Rolling Of Upper Arms

Fig 30

Fig 31

(e) Bring the right arm upward and backward (fig 30), breathing in once the arm is behind the body.

(f) Turn the body facing forward on equal leg weight and bring the right hand to the shoulder (fig 31), still breathing in.

Fig 32

Fig 33

(g) Push the right hand forward with erect palm in front of the chest, at the same time, withdrawing the left arm with palm facing upwards. The right palm cuts above the left palm (fig 32). Once right palm starts to push forward, breathing out.

(h) Repeat the left side as in fig 33, 34, 35, 36.

5. Fixed Stance With Back Rolling Of Upper Arms

Fig 34

Fig 35

Fig 36

6. To Row The Boat In The Middle Of The Lake

(a) Once the left palm cuts above the right palm, as in the previous posture, bring the two arms to shoulder width, with palms facing down and forward (fig 37).

Fig 37

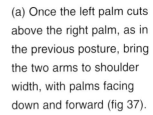

Fig 38

(b) Sink the body downwards to bring the arms to the sides of the body (fig 38), breathing out once the body starts to sink downward.

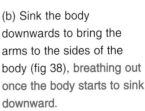
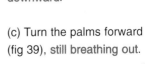

(c) Turn the palms forward (fig 39), still breathing out.

Fig 39

6. To Row The Boat In The Middle Of The Lake

(d) Raise the body and bring the arms up (can be from the sides of body or from slightly behind the body) (fig 40). Breathing in once you raise the body.

Fig 40

Fig 41

(e) Sink the body and bring the arms forwards with palm facing down (fig 41). Breathing out once the body starts to sink down.

(f) Bring the arms down until to the sides of body (fig 42), still breathing out.

Fig 42

7. To Carry A Ball In Front Of Shoulder

(a) Turn the right palm forward (fig 43) and get ready to breathe in.

(b) Raise the heels, waist turns left (about 45

Fig 43

Fig 44

degrees) and at the same time, raise the right arm to the left with palm facing upwards (fig 44). Breathe in once you turn the waist.

(c) Bring the heels down, turn the right palm down (fig 45).

Fig 45

7. To Carry A Ball In Front Of Shoulder

Fig 46

(d) Sink the body downwards and turn to face forwards. At the same time, bring the right arm down to the side of the body (fig 46). Breathe out once you start to sink body.

Fig 47

(e) Repeat on the left arm as in Fig 47, 48, 49 & 50.

Important:- Co-ordination of legs (raise and lower heels), body (waist turning left and right) and arms (up and down) needs continual practice and patience to achieve required results.

7. To Carry A Ball In Front Of Shoulder

Fig 48

Fig 49

Fig 50

8. To Turn The Body And Look At The Moon

Fig 51

(a) Place the arms in front of the body with palms facing each other (fig 51). The body still in a sinking position.

Fig 52

(b) Stand up slightly and raise the arms a little (fig 52). Breathe in once you start to raise the body.

(c) Turn waist to the left and bring both arms to the left side of the body with left hand higher than the right. Turn the head to the left and look at the left palm (fig 53). Still breathing in.

Fig 53

32

8. To Turn The Body And Look At The Moon

Important:- Do not raise the heels. In fig 53 the left arm should have a relaxed shoulder, elbow and wrist. Right palm facing left elbow.

Fig 54

Fig 55

(d) Return the waist to normal allowing the body to face forward again. At the same time, bring both arms down in front of body with palms facing each other. Body should sink down when turning the waist (fig 54). Breathe out once the body turns and sinks down.

(e) Repeat the movements on the other side (fig 55).

9. To Turn The Waist And Push The Palm

(a) From fig 55, breathe out once the waist turns back to normal; the body now faces forward. Sink the body and extend the arms to the front with both palms facing upwards (fig 56).

Fig 56

Fig 57

Fig 58

(b) Draw the palms to the waist (fig 57), breathing in during this movement.

(c) Raise the right palm to chest level (fig 58), still breathing in.

9. To Turn The Waist And Push The Palm

Fig 59

Fig 60

(d) Turn the waist left and push the right palm 45 degrees to the left at the same time, shift the body weight to the left (fig 59). Breathe out once you start to push the right palm.

(e) Turn the right palm to face up, at the same time, turn the waist to normal to bring the body facing forward. Draw the right palm to the right waist (fig 60). Breathe in once you start to draw in the right palm.

(f) Repeat the movement on the other side as in fig 61 and fig 62.

Fig 61

Fig 62

Important:- Both feet should be firm on the ground and shift your body weight in the direction where the palm pushes. The body should be in the 'sink down' position.

10. Horse Riding Stance With Cloud Hands

Fig 63

(a) From fig 62, turn the left palm to face yourself and the right arm extends out at the bottom (fig 63).

(b) Shift the weight to the centre and turn the body forward (fig 64). Breathe in once you shift the body.

(c) Shift the weight to the left foot and turn the waist to the left (fig 65). Still breathe in.

Fig 65

Fig 64

10. Horse Riding Stance With Cloud Hands

Fig 66

(d) Change the arm positions (fig 66). Still breathing in.

(e) Shift the weight to the centre and turn the body facing forwards (fig 67). Breathe out as you commence this movement.

(f) Shift the body weight to the right foot and turn the waist to the right (fig 68). Still breathing out.

Fig 67

Fig 68

11. To Scoop From The Sea To See The Sky

(a) Continue the previous movement. Using the right foot as a pivot, shift your weight completely to it. The waist turns left as you swing the left arm upwards to the left and extend right arm (fig 69 & 70).

Breathing in once you start to swing the left arm.

Fig 69

Fig 70

Important:- Weight is on the right foot, left toe on ground and body facing left at 45 degrees.

11. To Scoop From The Sea To See The Sky

(b) Put the left heel down
with left toes raised (fig 71),
still breathing in.

(c) Shift your weight to the
left and bend the body to
bring both arms down and
forward (fig 72). Breathing
out once you shift the
weight to the left and bend
down.

Fig 71

Fig 72

Important:- Body should be angled forward, with the top of
the head and the right foot on one straight line.

11. To Scoop From The Sea To See The Sky

Fig 73

Fig 74

(d) Continue bending the body forward as the palms cross in front with the right palm below the left, and both facing upward (fig 73), still breathing out.

(e) Weight back to the right foot with the body upright bringing both palms nearer the body (fig 74). Breathing in once you start to shift the weight from front to back (from left foot to right).

Fig 75

Fig 76

(f) Move the weight from back foot (right foot), to centre, and push the arms upward, palms still facing upwards until chest level (fig 75), still breathing in.

(g) Palms continue upward and turn to face forward (fig 76), still breathing in. Shift weight to the front and bend body to repeat the movement.

40

12. To Push The Wave And Tide

Fig 77

Fig 78

(a) Continue as fig 77.
(b) Shift weight to the front foot with toes of the back foot on the ground (back heel raised). At the same time, bring the arms from the top to the front with palms facing each other. The arms should be shoulder height and width (fig 78).
Breathing out once you start to shift the weight.

Fig 79

Fig 80

(c) Turn the palms to face down (fig 79), still breathing out.
(d) Fixing the back heel to the ground, start breathing in while slightly shifting body weight to the centre bringing arms downward with palm pressing down (fig 80).

12. To Push The Wave And Tide

Fig 81

(e) Continue drawing the body back so that the weight is now on the back foot with the front foot's toes being raised. At this stage, relax the wrists, bend the elbows and palms like a praying mantis (fig 81), still breathing in.

(f) Shift weight to centre, lower the toes and push the arms downward with palms facing down (fig 82). Breathing out once you start to shift weight.

Fig 82

Fig 83

(g) Continue shifting weight forward and raise the back heel. At the same time, bring both arms up and forward with wrists relaxed, and fingers facing downwards (fig 83), still breathing out.

Repeat the movement once you shift the weight backwards.

13 Flying Pigeon Spreading The Wings

(a) Continue from the previous movement. Turn the palms so fingers are facing each other and wrists relaxed (fig 84).

(b) Shift weight backwards firm the back foot and raise the front toe. At the same time, the body shifts backwards to open both arms breath in once you start to shift weight (fig 85).

Fig 84

Fig 85

13 Flying Pigeon Spreading The Wings

(c) The wrists open like door hinges to prepare the palms being brought forward (fig 86), still breathing in.

(d) Shift the weight forward with front toes firm and back heel raised. At the same time, bring the arms forward with palms facing each other (fig 87). Breathing out once your weight starts to shift forward.

Fig 86

Fig 87

Important:- Both arms should be relaxed with bent elbows and relaxed wrists. Arms brought to width of the body and wrists at shoulder height. Maintain straight posture with relaxed shoulders, elbows and wrists.

14. Horse Riding Stance With Punches

Fig 88

Fig 89

(a) Continue from the previous movement. Clench both fists (fig 88) still breathing out.

(b) Shift your weight to the back foot, with arms maintaining the same position (fig 89). Breath in once you start to shift weight to the back foot.

Fig 90

Fig 91

(c) Turn the body forwards and bring the left foot parallel with the right. Both feet holding equal weight. Arms still maintaining the same position (fig 90). Still breathing in.

(d) Body at horse riding stance and draw in both fists to the waist (fig 91), still breathing in.

14. Horse Riding Stance With Punches

(e) Raise the left fist to the chest (fig 92), still breathing in.

(f) Punch with left fist to the front, reversing the wrist while extending the arm (fig 93). Breathing out once you start punching.

(g) Turn the left fist facing upwards and withdraw the left waist (fig 94). Breathing in once you start to withdraw the fist.

(h) Repeat with right fist as fig 95 and 96.

Important:- Maintain equal weight on both feet. The punching should be in a relaxed manner. Do not fully straighten the arms when punching.

15. Wild Goose Flying

(a) Continue from the previous movement. After punching, open both palms facing upward (fig 97), still breathing out.

(b) Sink the body down bringing arms to the sides of the thighs (fig 98), still breathing out.

(c) Raise both heels with the body coming up to bring both arms from sides of body to above the head (fig 99). As you raise the heels start to breathe in.

15. Wild Goose Flying

Fig 100

(d) Lower heels to the ground (fig 100).

Fig 101

(e) Sink the body down and bring both arms downwards from the sides to the thighs (fig 101). Breathe out as you begin to sink the body.

> **Important**:- Raise the heels before raising the body and firm the heels before sinking the body, ensuring stability in your posture.
>
> The up and down of both arms are like a wild goose flapping both wings.

16.To Turn Like A Flying Wheel

Fig 102

Fig 103

(a) From the previous posture when the body is raised and the arms are at the top (fig 102). Breathing in during the process.

(b) Firm the heels and shift the weight to the right foot with the body turning slightly to the right (fig 103), still breathing in.

Fig 104

Fig 105

(c) Sink the body down with the weight on the right foot and bring both arms down on the right side of the body (fig 104). Breathing out as the body starts to sink.

(d) Stand up slightly and bring both arms to the top (fig 105). Shift the body weight from the right side to the left, while the body turns slightly left. Breathe in once you start to stand up.

16.To Turn Like A Flying Wheel

(e) Turn the body to face
forward and shift the weight
to the centre with both legs
carrying equal weight. At
the same time, both arms
are at the top (fig 106), still
breathing in.

Repeat the above
movements a few times
before proceeding to the
next movement.

Fig 106

(f) Continue from the last
posture. Sink the body
down with the weight on the
right foot and bring both
arms down on the right side
of the body (fig 107).
Breathe out once the body
starts to sink down.

Fig 107

(g) Shift the weight to the
left foot with the body
turning slightly to the left
side and bring both arms to
the left (fig 108), still
breathing out.

(h) Shift the weight to the
right, while the body turns
slightly right and bring both
arms to the right (fig 109),
still breathe out.

Fig 108

16.To Turn Like A Flying Wheel

Fig 109

Fig 110

(i) Stand up slightly and bring both arms to the top. Body weight is still on the right (fig 110). Breathe in once you start to stand up.

(j)Turn the body to face forward and shift the weight to the centre (fig 111), still breathe in.

Fig 111

Fig 112

(k) Shift the weight to the left foot, still breathing in. Sink the body down with the weight on left foot and bring both arms down to the left side of the body (fig 112). Breathing out once your body starts to sink down.

Repeat the above movement a few times.

Important:- Maintain a straight posture. Arms must be relaxed. Using the body (up and down) and the shifting weight to move both arms.

17. To Bounce Ball With Raised Leg

Fig 113

(a) Continue from the previous posture. Shift the weight to the right and bring both arms in front of the body (fig 113), still breathing out.

(b) Firm the right foot, raise the left foot and the right hand and simulate a bouncing ball movement (fig 114), breathing in when bouncing the ball with the right hand.

Fig 114

(c) Put the left foot down and shift the weight to the left, raise the right foot and left hand, then with the left hand simulate a bouncing ball movement (fig 115). Breathing out when bouncing the ball with left hand.

Fig 115

Repeat the right and left movement above.

Important:- Firm the one foot before lifting the other foot.

18. To Press Palms In Calmness

(a) Continue from the previous movement.

(b) Sink the body down and place both palms further downwards (fig 116), still breathing out.

Fig 116

Fig 117

(c) Raise the body, turn the palms up and bring the arms upwards and near the body at the same time (fig 117). Breathing in once you start to raise the body.

(d) Continue raising the body and bring the arms to chest level (fig 118), still breathing in.

Fig 118

18. To Press Palms In Calmness

Fig 119

(e) Turn the palms downward (fig 119), still breathing in

(f) Sink the body and push the palms downwards in front of the body (fig 120). Breathe out once the body starts to sink down.

Fig 120

Fig 121

(g) Continue the sinking of the body and bring the arms and palms down even further (fig 121). Continue breathing out.

18. To Press Palms In Calmness

Fig 122

Fig 123

(h) Raise the body, turn the palms and bring the arms up (fig 122). Breathing in once standing up.

Repeat the above a few times.

(i) Continue from the previous movement. Turn the palms (fig 123) still breathing in.

Fig 124

Fig 125

(j)This time do not sink the body but just press both palms downward (fig 124). Breathing out once you start to press the palms down.

(k) Continue pressing down the palms and turn them so they face the stomach (fig 125). Hold this posture for one or two minutes to cool down. Breathe naturally.

The Journey of a Thousand Miles Begins with a First Step...

the First Steps *series*

- First Steps to Meditation
- First Steps to Massage
- First Steps to Tarot
- First Steps to Chi Kung
- First Steps to Dream Power
- First Steps to Yoga

  Further titles following shortly:

- First Steps to Reflexology
- First Steps to Feng Shui
- First Steps to Managing Stress
- First Steps to Astrology
- First Steps to Chinese Herbal Medicine
- First Steps to Acupressure

  First Steps to...

- **AXIOM PUBLISHING**
Unit 2, 1 Union Street, Stepney, South Australia, 5069